EARLY AMERICA: LIFE STORIES

YOUNG BENJAMIN FRANKLIN

1. A STUDIOUS BOY

Benjamin Franklin was born in Boston on the 17th of January, 1706. His parents were poor people who lived in a humble home on Milk Street, and he was the youngest son in the family of seventeen children.

Little Benjamin learned to read almost as soon as he could talk. He was so bright and studious that his parents wished to educate him for the ministry. When he was eight years old, they sent him to the Latin School where boys were prepared for Harvard College. He learned very fast and soon made his way to the head of his class. But his father had little money, and could not afford to keep Benjamin in school. So they gave up the plan of educating Benjamin to be a preacher.

After leaving the Latin School, Benjamin went to a school where he learned to write and to calculate—two skills necessary to one who was to follow a trade. When he was ten years old he was taken out of school altogether. Although so young, there were many things he could do, and his father needed his help.

Mr. Franklin was a candle maker, and for two years he kept Benjamin busy cutting wicks, molding candles, and waiting on customers. But the lad did not like the business. When he saw the ships come into the harbor with their cargoes of goods from strange lands beyond the sea, he thought that he would like above all things to be a sailor.

American Lives
and Legends

TABLE OF CONTENTS

EARLY AMERICA: LIFE STORIES

AMERICAN LEGENDS: STORIES OF WASHINGTON IRVING

But his father objected to this and kept him in the shop more closely than ever. Then he turned his attention to books.

Benjamin could find no books written especially for children, because there were few if any to be found. Still, he read all the books he could get hold of. Sometimes he would borrow a volume and sit up nearly all night reading it so as to return it promptly.

When James Franklin, one of Benjamin's brothers, set up a printing press in Boston, his father said, "Here is a chance for Benjamin. He is a lover of books. He shall learn to be a printer." And so, at the age of twelve years, the lad was apprenticed to his brother to learn the printer's trade.

James Franklin's press published a newspaper called the *New England Courant.* It was the fourth newspaper published in America.

Benjamin Franklin found his brother to be a hard master. James was always finding fault with his workmen. Sometimes he would beat young Benjamin or shout at him for no reason.

When Benjamin was nearly seventeen years of age, he decided he would not endure this treatment any longer. He told his brother that he meant to leave him and find work with someone else.

His brother was alarmed. He went to all the other printers in Boston and warned them not to employ the lad. Their father took the elder brother's part, and scolded Benjamin for being so hard to please. But Benjamin was determined that he would do no more work in James's printing house.

2. In Search of Work

Since he could not find employment in Boston, Benjamin decided he would run away from home. He would go to New York and look for work there.

He sold his books to raise a little money. Then, without saying good-bye to his father or mother or any of his brothers or sisters, he went on board of a ship that was just ready to sail from the harbor.

It is not likely that he was very happy while doing this. Long afterwards he said, "I reckon this as one of the first *errata* of my life."

What did he mean by *errata*? Errata are mistakes—mistakes that sometimes cannot be easily corrected.

Three days after leaving Boston, Franklin arrived in New York. It was then October, in the year 1723. The lad had but very little money in his pocket. He knew no one in New York. He was three hundred miles from home and friends.

As soon as he landed, he went about the streets, looking for work. New York was only a little town then, and there was not a newspaper in it. There were only a few printing shops, and these had little work to do. The boy from Boston asked at every place, but he found that nobody wanted to employ any more help.

At one of the little shops, Franklin was told that perhaps he would find work in Philadelphia. Philadelphia at that time was a larger and much more important place than New York.

Franklin decided to go there without delay. It would be easier to do this than to give up and try to return to Boston. But Philadelphia was one hundred miles farther from home, and one hundred miles was a very great distance in those days.

There are two ways of going from New York to Philadelphia. One way is by sea. The other is by land, across New Jersey.

As Franklin had but little money, he decided to take the shorter route by land. But he sent his little chest, containing his best clothes, round by sea in a boat.

He walked all the way from Perth Amboy, on the eastern shore of New Jersey, to Burlington on the Delaware River. Nowadays you may travel that distance in about an hour, for it is little more than fifty miles. But at that time there were no railroads, and for nearly three days Franklin trudged along lonely wagon tracks in a pouring rain.

At Burlington he was lucky enough to be taken on board a small boat going down the river. Burlington is not more than thirty miles above Philadelphia. But the boat moved very slowly, and as there was no wind, the men took turns at rowing.

Night came on, and they were afraid that they might pass by Philadelphia in the darkness. So they landed and camped on the shore, among the reeds and bushes, until morning.

Early the next day, which chanced to be Sunday, they arrived at Philadelphia. Benjamin Franklin stepped on shore at Market Street.

No one who saw him could have guessed that he would one day be the greatest man in the city. He was indeed a sorry-looking fellow. He was dressed in his working clothes, and was very dirty from being so long on the road and in the little boat.

Here is the story of what happened to him on that first day in Philadelphia, as Benjamin Franklin told it in his own words.

3. THAT FIRST DAY IN PHILADELPHIA
from The Autobiography of Benjamin Franklin

I was in my working dress, my best clothes being to come round by sea. I was dirty from my journey; my pockets were stuffed out with shirts and stockings, and I knew no soul or where to look for lodging. I was fatigued with traveling, rowing, and want of rest; I was very hungry; and my whole stock of cash consisted of a Dutch dollar and about a shilling in copper.

The latter I gave the people of the boat for my passage, who at first refused it on account of my rowing; but I insisted on their taking it. A man is sometimes more generous when he has but a little money than when he has plenty, perhaps through fear of being thought to have but little. Then I walked up a street, gazing about, till, near the market house, I met a boy with bread.

I had made many a meal on bread, and, inquiring where he had bought it, I went immediately to the baker's he directed me to, in Second Street, and asked for biscuit, intending such as we had in Boston; but they, it seems, were not made in Philadelphia.

Then I asked for a threepenny loaf, and was told they had none such. So, not knowing the difference of money, or the greatest cheapness or the names of his bread, I bade him give me threepenny-worth of any sort.

He gave me, accordingly, three great, puffy rolls. I was surprised at the quantity, but took it, and having no room in my pockets, walked off with a roll under each arm and eating the other.

Thus I went up Market Street as far as Fourth Street, passing by the door of Mr. Reed, my future wife's father; when she, standing at the door, saw me and thought I made, as I certainly did, a most awkward and ridiculous appearance.

I then turned and went down Chestnut Street and part of Walnut Street, eating my roll all the way. Coming round, I found myself again near the boat I came in, to which I went for a draft of the river water; and one of my rolls having satisfied me, I gave the other two to a woman and her child who had come down the river in the boat with us, and were waiting to go further.

Thus refreshed, I walked again up the street, which by this time had many clean-dressed people in it who were all walking the same way. I joined them, and thereby was led to a great meetinghouse of the Quakers near the market.

I sat down among them, and, after looking round awhile and hearing nothing said, being drowsy through labor and want of rest the preceding night, I fell fast asleep and continued so till the meeting broke up, when one was kind enough to rouse me. This was, therefore, the first house I was in, or slept in, in Philadelphia.

4. The Value of Time

Benjamin Franklin soon found a job with a printer. And not long after, he opened his own print shop. He also sold books.

A busy and hardworking man, Franklin fully understood the value of time, and had little patience for those who wasted it. He wrote, "Dost thou love life? Then do not squander time, for that is the stuff life is made of."

In his *Autobiography*, Benjamin Franklin tells a story that shows how much he valued time. Here is the story (though not in Franklin's own words).

One day, a customer came into Franklin's little bookstore in Philadelphia. He asked to know the price of a book. The clerk told him. The customer was dissatisfied.

"Please call the proprietor," he said to the clerk. "I wish to ask him about this."

"Mr. Franklin is in the press room," answered the clerk, "and he is very busy just now."

The man, however, who had already spent an hour in aimlessly turning over many books, insisted on seeing him.

Mr. Franklin hurried out from the printing office at the back of the store and came in to see what was wanted.

"What is the lowest price you can take for this book, sir?" asked the customer, holding up the volume he had chosen.

"One dollar and a quarter," Franklin promptly replied.

"A dollar and a quarter! Why, your clerk offered it to me a little while ago for only a dollar," cried the astonished customer.

"True," said Franklin, "and I could have afforded to take a dollar rather than leave my work and get a dollar and a quarter."

The man hesitated and looked at the book again. He was in doubt whether Mr. Franklin was in earnest or only joking. Then he said, coaxingly, "Come now, Mr. Franklin, tell me really, what is the lowest price for this book?"

"One dollar and a half," was the grave reply.

"A dollar and a half! Why, a minute ago you offered it to me for a dollar and a quarter."

"Yes, and I could better have taken that price then than a dollar and a half now."

The crestfallen customer laid the money on the counter and left the store with his book. Perhaps he had learned that he who squanders his own time is foolish and he who wastes the time of others is a thief.

5. ADVICE FROM POOR RICHARD

In 1733, Benjamin Franklin started publishing an almanac, a book that comes out once a year. An almanac is full of information, such as calendars, recipes, and predictions about the weather.

In *Poor Richard's Almanac*, Franklin also offered something else—advice, and lots of it. In the voice of a character named Richard Saunders, Franklin wrote many humorous and practical proverbs. Many people still repeat these sayings today.

Here is a sampling of the wit and wisdom of Poor Richard.

- A penny saved is a penny earned.

- Early to bed and early to rise, makes a man healthy, wealthy, and wise.

- Little strokes fell great oaks.

- Don't throw stones at your neighbors', if your own windows are glass.

- He that speaks much, is much mistaken.

- An ounce of prevention is worth a pound of cure.

- Eat to live, and not live to eat.

- Fish and visitors stink in three days.

- Three may keep a secret, if two of them are dead.

- God helps them that help themselves.

- Well done is better than well said.

- A lie stands on one leg, truth on two.

- A true friend is the best possession.

- When the well's dry, we know the worth of water.

- Lost time is never found again.

- There are no gains without pains.

- Have you something to do tomorrow? Do it today.

- The noblest question in the world is, What good may I do in it?

- Hear no ill of a friend, nor speak any of an enemy.

- Whatever is begun in anger ends in shame.

- Being ignorant is not so much a shame as being unwilling to learn.

PHILLIS WHEATLEY: A POEM TO KING GEORGE

by Kathryn Kilby Borland and Helen Ross Speicher

In 1761 the Wheatley family of Boston purchased a slave at auction. The frail seven-year-old girl, who had been taken from her home in West Africa, learned to speak English quickly. The Wheatley family, who named the girl Phillis, taught her to read and write—which was unusual for slaves at the time. Within less than two years, Phillis was reading the Bible, Greek and Roman myths, history, poetry, and more. And, as the following story shows, she was soon writing poems of her own.

Phillis sat up in bed. It wasn't daylight. Some sound must have awakened her, but the night was quiet again. She lay back and closed her eyes, wondering whether she was mistaken. Then she heard a bell ringing, again and again, louder and louder.

She ran to open her window and leaned out into the warm May darkness. Far down the street she could hear a horse's hoofbeats. Then a man on horseback came galloping down the street. He was shouting, but Phillis could not understand what he said.

Now she could hear Mr. Wheatley's window being thrown up with an angry sound. "What's all this?" he called out crossly.

"Good news! Good news!" the horseman shouted, but he didn't slow down.

Phillis noticed lighted windows in other houses up and down the street. One or two men had come out on the front steps with dressing gowns over their nightshirts.

"What is it?" they called to one another, but nobody seemed to know.

Before long a group of young men came running down the street with lighted torches. They were throwing their hats in the air.

"Three cheers for King George! Three cheers for the Sons of Liberty!" they shouted. Finally Mr. Wheatley got the attention of one of the young men.

"We have good news about the Stamp Act, sir," the man called. "Word just came that the Stamp Act has been repealed!"

Phillis could hear Nat's shout from his room. "We did it! We did it!"

No one in the Wheatley household, or probably in all of Boston, went back to sleep that night. The bells went on ringing. Soon drums were beating steadily, and once in a while the boom of a canon could be heard.

Breakfast next morning was a happy meal. Everyone was hungry after the excitement of the night. Sukey beamed as she brought in huge platters of codfish cakes and corn bread.

"Well," Mrs. Wheatley said, "from now on Boston should be the way it used to be. No more riots. No more Sons of Liberty."

"Oh, I think we'll still have the Sons of Liberty, Mother," Nat said. "We want to be sure England doesn't try anything else."

"Don't speak of England as if it were a foreign country, Nat," his father said. "We shall always be English."

"Of course we will, Father, no matter where we live. But we want to be treated like all other Englishmen."

The clock in the hall struck eight, and still Mr. Wheatley sat at the table with his family. "Aren't you going to the shop today, John?" Mrs. Wheatley asked.

"Precious little trade I would have today," Mr. Wheatley replied. "This will be a holiday in all of Boston."

"Can Nat take Phillis and me out to see the excitement?" Mary asked.

"Certainly he can, unless he has other plans," Mr. Wheatley answered.

"No, not really," Nat answered slowly. Phillis was sure Nat would rather have gone by himself, but he seldom could bring himself to hurt anyone's feelings.

By the time Mary and Phillis were ready, crowds of people were filling the narrow streets. Most of them were dressed in their best Sunday clothes. Flags were waving from many of the houses, and everybody was laughing.

As Nat, Mary, and Phillis turned toward the Commons, Phillis said, "Oh, look at the Liberty Tree. Isn't it exciting?" The enormous elm tree had been named the Liberty Tree because it was one of the favorite meeting places of the Sons of Liberty. Now flags and colored streamers of every color hung from its branches. They looked as if they had grown there, but of course some people had worked hard to put them there during the night.

The celebration lasted all day. Bands wandered through the crowds, playing loudly if not well. The bells kept ringing.

That night there was a fireworks display on the Commons. There had never been such fireworks in Boston. The air was filled with rockets, bright serpents, and spinning pinwheels. At eleven o'clock twenty-one rockets and sixteen dozen serpents were sent up all at once for a glorious finish.

A loud cheer went up for King George. Phillis wished that King George could know how happy the people were about what had been done. She wished someone would tell him.

After Phillis went to bed that night she tossed and turned. Some idea was trying to form in her brain, but she was too tired to think about it. In the middle of the night the idea suddenly came to her.

She would write King George about how the colonists felt. Perhaps she could even write it in verse. She had written a poem not long before, but had not shown it to anyone.

She crept quietly out of bed and her candle burned for hours while she wrote. When she woke up in the morning she looked at what she had written. What a ridiculous idea, she thought. How could I ever have imagined that the king would read anything written by a young servant girl? She left the poem on the little table by her bed and almost forgot it.

A few weeks later Phillis was sick in bed with a cold. One morning Mrs. Wheatley brought a bowl of porridge for her breakfast. As she set the bowl on the little table, she noticed a scrap of paper there. She picked up the paper and asked, "What is this, Phillis?"

Phillis was embarrassed. "Oh, it's nothing, Mrs. Wheatley, nothing at all."

"But it is, Phillis. These are beautiful words. Did you copy this poem from a book?"

"Oh, no, Mrs. Wheatley. I wrote it myself, but it really isn't very good."

"You wrote it yourself? Phillis, this is remarkable. Why didn't you show it to us?"

"I was ashamed to show it to you, Mrs. Wheatley. I actually wrote it to send to the king, and then I decided that would be silly. Besides the poem isn't any good."

"May I show it to Mr. Wheatley?"

Phillis hesitated. Probably Mr. Wheatley would think the poem was foolish. But she said, "Yes, of course," and Mrs. Wheatley did not seem to notice her lack of enthusiasm.

That evening after supper the whole family came up to her room. Mr. Wheatley was holding the poem in his hand. He looked very solemn, and Phillis feared he was angry. Then he cleared his throat and said, "Mrs. Wheatley tells me you wrote this poem."

"Yes, sir," Phillis answered feebly.

"Now are you sure you really wrote it yourself? Sometimes we read something and don't remember it. Later we remember it but don't remember where we saw it. Then we may think we thought of it ourselves. Do you see what I mean, Phillis?"

"Yes, sir, I do," Phillis said. "But that isn't the way it was this time. I wanted to make King George see how grateful we were. This was the only way I could think of. I know it was foolish of me, sir. I guess I was just excited over the celebration."

"I told you, Father," Mary said. "Phillis reads and reads and reads. She uses words I don't even know how to use."

Mr. Wheatley cleared his throat again. "Well, then," he said, "in that case it's remarkable. Have you written any other poems?"

"Yes, sir. I wrote one about Harvard College. Would you like to see it?"

A few minutes later Mr. Wheatley left the room with both poems in his hand. Then one evening several days later he told Phillis that she was to go to the State House with him the next morning. "A few gentlemen there would like to ask you about your poems."

"They'll be angry," Phillis thought. "Mr. Wheatley shouldn't have told them."

Usually Phillis enjoyed the gilded lion and unicorn over the State House door. Today she was too frightened even to look at them. Mr. Wheatley had told her that the most important men in Boston would talk with her.

Mr. Wheatley led her into the Council Chamber. Several stern-looking men who were seated at a long table looked up at her. Others looked down from gold frames on the wall.

"Stand at this end of the table where we can see you," one of the men said. He was holding her poems in his hand.

"Yes, sir," Phillis said in a low voice. She folded her hands in front of her to stop them from shaking.

"Mr. Wheatley tells us you wrote these poems," said one of the men.

"Yes, sir."

"Did anyone give you any help?"

"No, sir."

"Why did you write about Harvard College?"

"Because, sir, Mr. Nat brought back so much from there for Miss Mary and me to study and talk about. He even taught Latin to Miss Mary, and she taught it to me."

"Latin, eh?" a man said with interest. "Can you tell me what *E pluribus unum* means?"

Phillis smiled. "Yes, sir. It means 'one from many,'" she said.

Some of the other gentlemen asked questions in Latin, which she was able to answer. They also asked her what books she liked to read. Then they began asking about her poems.

"Tell us what you meant by these lines:

> *May every clime with equal gladness see*
> *A monarch's smile can set his subjects free.*"

The speaker was Mr. Samuel Adams. Phillis had often seen him at the Wheatley's house. "I meant that we were glad the king used his power to make us happy. I'm sorry the meaning wasn't clear, sir," she said.

"I think it was quite clear."

The other gentlemen nodded. They asked her questions almost all morning. She was so tired before they were through that she hardly knew what she answered.

At the end of the questioning, Mr. Adams smiled and said, "We shall send your poem to the king, and we hope that you will write many more. You have a great gift, young woman, a very great gift, and it must be used."

Phillis Wheatley kept on writing poems. In 1773, a publisher in London published a book with 39 of her poems, called Poems on Various Subjects, Religious and Moral. *It is the first book of poetry to be published by an African American. The book included the poem she wrote to King George, called "To the King's Most Excellent Majesty":*

YOUR subjects hope, dread Sire,
The crown upon your brows may flourish long,
And that your arm may in your God be strong.
Oh, may your sceptre num'rous nations sway,
And all with love and readiness obey.

But how shall we the British king reward?
Rule thou in peace, our father and our lord!
'Midst the remembrance of thy favors past,
The meanest peasants most admire the last.

May George, beloved by all the nations round,
Live with heaven's choicest, constant blessings crowned.
Great God! direct and guard him from on high,
And from his head let every evil fly;
And may each clime with equal gladness see
A monarch's smile can set his subjects free.

PAUL REVERE'S RIDE
by Henry Wadsworth Longfellow

One night in April of 1775, three men mounted fast horses and rode to warn their fellow colonists in Massachusetts, "The redcoats are coming!" These three men were Patriots—colonists who wanted independence from British rule.

One of these three Patriots was a silversmith named Paul Revere. Why do we remember Paul Revere more than his fellow riders, William Dawes and Dr. Samuel Prescott? Because of the famous poem written by Henry Wadsworth Longfellow.

Why did Paul Revere and his companions want to warn the colonists?

At this time, on the eve of the American Revolution, many colonists wanted to be independent of Britain, but they hoped to gain independence by peaceful means. After all, England was a strong nation with a powerful army and navy. But the colonies were a scattered group, not really organized or ready for a great fight.

Still, the colonists knew that war might come. So, to prepare, some colonists had gathered weapons and hidden them in the town of Concord, Massachusetts.

The British heard about the hidden weapons and decided to seize them. But Paul Revere and his friends heard that the British were preparing to march on Concord.

Paul Revere had already asked a friend to alert him about the movements of the British. When his friend saw which way the British were taking, he was to climb to the steeple of the Old North Church in Boston. The signal was, "One if by land, two if by sea"—which meant, shine one light if the British are marching by

land, or two lights if they are coming in boats across the bay.
Here, then, is the famous poem that has kept Paul Revere alive in
the American memory.

Listen, my children, and you shall hear
Of the midnight ride of Paul Revere,
On the eighteenth of April, in Seventy-five;
Hardly a man is now alive
Who remembers that famous day and year.

He said to his friend, "If the British march
By land or sea from the town tonight,
Hang a lantern aloft in the belfry arch
Of the North Church tower as a signal light—
One if by land, and two if by sea;
And I on the opposite shore will be,
Ready to ride and spread the alarm
Through every Middlesex village and farm,
For the country folk to be up and to arm."

Then he said, "Good night!" and with muffled oar
Silently rowed to the Charlestown shore,
Just as the moon rose over the bay,
Where swinging wide at her mooring lay
The *Somerset*, British man-of-war;
A phantom ship, with each mast and spar
Across the moon like a prison bar,
And a huge black hulk, that was magnified
By its own reflection in the tide.

Meanwhile, his friend, through alley and street,
Wanders and watches, with eager ears,
Till in the silence around him he hears

The muster of men at the barrack door,
The sound of arms, and the tramp of feet,
And the measured tread of the grenadiers,
Marching down to their boats on the shore.
Then he climbed to the tower of the Old North Church,
By the wooden stairs, with stealthy tread,
To the belfry chamber overhead,
And startled the pigeons from their perch
On the somber rafters, that round him made
Masses and moving shapes of shade—
By the trembling ladder, steep and tall,
To the highest window in the wall,
Where he paused to listen and look down
A moment on the roofs of the town,
And the moonlight flowing over all.

Beneath in the churchyard, lay the dead,
In their night encampment on the hill,
Wrapped in the silence so deep and still
That he could hear, like a sentinel's tread,
The watchful night-wind, as it went
Creeping along from tent to tent,
And seeming to whisper, "All is well!"
A moment only he feels the spell
Of the place and the hour, and the secret dread
Of the lonely belfry and the dead;
For suddenly all his thoughts are bent
On a shadowy something far away,
Where the river widens to meet the bay—
A line of black that bends and floats
On the rising tide, like a bridge of boats.

Meanwhile, impatient to mount and ride,
Booted and spurred, with a heavy stride
On the opposite shore walked Paul Revere.
Now he patted his horse's side,
Now gazed at the landscape far and near,
Then, impetuous, stamped the earth,
And turned and tightened his saddle girth;
But mostly he watched with eager search
The belfry tower of the Old North Church,
As it rose above the graves on the hill,
Lonely and spectral and somber and still.
And lo! as he looks, on the belfry's height
A glimmer, and then a gleam of light!
He springs to the saddle, the bridle he turns,
But lingers and gazes, till full on his sight
A second lamp in the belfry burns!

A hurry of hoofs in a village street,
A shape in the moonlight, a bulk in the dark,
And beneath, from the pebbles, in passing, a spark
Struck out by a steed flying fearless and fleet:
That was all! And yet, through the gloom and the light,
The fate of a nation was riding that night;
And the spark struck out by the steed, in his flight,
Kindled the land into flame with its heat.

He has left the village and mounted the steep,
And beneath him, tranquil and broad and deep,
Is the Mystic, meeting the ocean tides;
And under the alders that skirt its edge,
Now soft on the sand, now loud on the ledge,
Is heard the tramp of his steed as he rides.

It was twelve by the village clock,
When he crossed the bridge into Medford town.
He heard the crowing of the cock,
And the barking of the farmer's dog,
And felt the damp of the river fog,
That rises after the sun goes down.

It was one by the village clock,
When he galloped into Lexington.
He saw the gilded weathercock
Swim in the moonlight as he passed,
And the meeting-house windows, blank and bare,
Gaze at him with a spectral glare,
As if they already stood aghast
At the bloody work they would look upon.

It was two by the village clock,
When he came to the bridge in Concord town.

He heard the bleating of the flock,
And the twitter of birds among the trees,
And felt the breath of the morning breeze
Blowing over the meadows brown.
And one was safe and asleep in his bed
Who at the bridge would be the first to fall,
Who that day would be lying dead,
Pierced by a British musket ball.

You know the rest. In the books you have read
How the British Regulars fired and fled—
How the farmers gave them ball for ball,
From behind each fence and farmyard wall,
Chasing the redcoats down the lane,
Then crossing the fields to emerge again
Under the trees at the turn of the road,
And only pausing to fire and load.

So through the night rode Paul Revere;
And so through the night went his cry of alarm
To every Middlesex village and farm—
A cry of defiance and not of fear,
A voice in the darkness, a knock at the door,
And a word that shall echo forevermore!
For, borne on the night wind of the Past,
Through all our history, to the last,
In the hour of darkness and peril and need,
The people will awaken and listen to hear
The hurrying hoof-beats of that steed,
And the midnight message of Paul Revere.

Sybil Ludington:
The Female Paul Revere
by Patricia Edwards Clyne

"Will Papa stay home this time?"

Sybil Ludington smiled as she tucked the covers around the boy. Each of her seven brothers and sisters had asked the same question at least twice since Colonel Ludington had come home from war.

"He'll be here for a while," Sybil told her youngest brother. "The men have been given only enough time to do their spring planting."

"Then Papa will have to go back again?"

"Yes, the war is far from over," she replied with a sigh. "Now, close those eyes. I must get back downstairs, for I hear a horse coming into the mill yard."

The boy listened for a moment, then said, "Maybe it's General Washington!"

"Not likely," Sybil laughed. "He's probably gone home to Virginia to do his spring planting, too. Now, no more of your delaying tactics, young man. Good night!"

Her brother grinned in good-natured defeat. "Night, Syb," he called, for she was already on her way downstairs.

Before she reached the large kitchen, Sybil could hear the drumlike sound of a heavy fist on the front door.

"Colonel Ludington! Colonel Ludington!" a voice cried out urgently. "The British are raiding Danbury!"

Sybil raced into the room just as the exhausted messenger was being led to a chair by the fire.

"Why, Danbury's less than thirty miles to the east!" she exclaimed. But neither of the two men even noticed her presence.

Her grim-faced father was listening intently as the messenger related that Danbury, Connecticut, had been left virtually unprotected. When the American troops were dismissed to take care of the spring planting, only 150 militiamen had remained behind to guard the storehouses of the Continental Army. This small force could do little to stem the onrushing tide of the enemy. Even now, General William Tryon's 2,000 troops were looting and burning the town.

"We must immediately recall our men from their farms!" Colonel Ludington declared. "Everyone must be warned, for the British may not stop at Danbury. They may decide to raid here as well. We'll have the men meet here at the mill. As soon as they arrive, I ..."

Sybil's father stopped suddenly when he realized the spent condition of the man before him. With a worried frown, he went on, "But who will summon the men? You're too exhausted to ride farther. And I must stay here to muster the men as they arrive. There is no one else who ..."

"I can!" Sybil's voice rang out. "I will sound the alarm."

"A sixteen-year-old girl?" Colonel Ludington almost gasped, then began shaking his head negatively. "The night is dark and the roads unsafe—Tories and brigands infest every byway."

"I know all the farms. I can do it!" Sybil insisted.

"But daughter, it would be many miles—many dark and dangerous miles. I cannot permit ..."

"Father," Sybil broke in, "the people must be warned—and there simply is no one else to do it."

Before Colonel Ludington could answer, Sybil had rushed outside to the shed where the horses were kept. Within minutes, she had slipped a bridle over her favorite horse's head. After firmly cinching the saddle, she leaped on his back.

Colonel Ludington was standing outside as she rode up. There was worry—but also a touch of pride—in his voice when he told his daughter, "Remember, the men are to muster here at the mill. Also tell the women to gather their valuables and be ready to move out at a moment's notice should Tryon get this far."

Sybil nodded as she prodded her mount with the small stick she carried. The horse's hoofs sounded like thunder on the frost-hardened ground. Soon the lights of the Ludington house were swallowed up by the dark trees that arched the road behind her.

Even though it was late April, the night was chill and Sybil was shivering by the time she reached the first farmhouse. Without dismounting, she called, "The British are burning Danbury! Muster at Colonel Ludington's mill! Prepare for a British raid!"

The startled farmer who appeared at the door did not seem to comprehend, so Sybil shouted her message again, then galloped off.

She traveled south toward Carmel, crying out her warning at each farm. Then on to Lake Mahopac. There were no lights burning in the homes now, for the hour was late. Without these small and welcoming beacons, Sybil felt her courage faltering, and she fought back the tears of fear as she rode on.

All too well she remembered the stories of the notorious "cowboys" who roamed the area. Though they professed to be helping the British, the cowboys were really only lawless murderers who plundered outlying districts for their own selfish gain.

For one swift moment, Sybil felt like turning back. But the reality of the British at Danbury was much more frightening than the possibility of meeting any cowboys, and she rode on.

The coldness of the April night had numbed her hands and feet by the time she reached Tompkins Corners, and the horse's breath was rasping. She knew it would be impossible to reach each and every home in the area, but the ones she did notify could warn the others.

Farmer's Mills was a few minutes behind her when she felt her horse falter. He was tiring now, she realized, and well he might, for they had already covered nearly thirty miles.

"Only a little while longer," she consoled the laboring animal, as well as herself.

Over and over her cry was heard, so that by the time Sybil left Pecksville on her way home, her voice was no more than a hoarse croak. But she had done it. She had warned her neighbors of the British threat!

The Ludington mill yard was full of men when Sybil guided the weary horse through the front gate. In the flurry of preparing for the march to Danbury, there was little more than a hurried, "Well done, Sybil." But in quieter days, when the British had finally been driven from the land, the story of Sybil Ludington's heroic ride would be repeated with pride, and she would be remembered forever afterward as "The Female Paul Revere."

(Note: General Tryon's troops never got as far as Putnam County, New York, where Sybil Ludington made her historic midnight ride. Thanks to the prompt mustering of the militia, the British were halted at Ridgefield, Connecticut, on April 27, 1777, and were forced to retreat to their ships in Long Island Sound.)

Sequoyah's Great Invention

Think about the things you can do with writing.

You can write your name. You can write a letter to a friend. You can write a list of things that you need to get the next time you go grocery shopping.

Now, imagine if there were no writing. Imagine that you could only speak your words, but that there was no way to write them down.

There would be no books. People could tell stories, but they couldn't write them down. There would be no newspapers to tell us about important things happening nearby and around the world. There would be no signs on the road to tell drivers to "Stop" or "Slow Down— Construction Ahead."

No one would ever receive a letter from a friend or relative. No one could even stick a little note on the refrigerator saying, "Don't forget to feed the neighbor's cat."

You can see how important writing is, and how it helps us do so many things.

There was once a Cherokee man named Sequoyah, and, like you, he understood how important writing is.

Let's imagine Sequoyah as a young boy, sitting with his family and friends around a blazing campfire and listening to someone tell wonderful stories about the brave deeds of Cherokee warriors, or how the world began, or why corn grows.

Sequoyah listens very carefully. He wants to remember the stories. He squeezes his eyes closed tight and tries with all his might to remember each and every word.

Why does he try so hard to remember the stories? Because he has no way of writing them down. Back then, the Cherokee did not have a way to write down their own language.

When Sequoyah grew to be a young man, he could speak many languages. He spoke his own Cherokee language, of course, but he also learned Spanish and French.

Sequoyah was fascinated by the way that the Spanish and French settlers could write their words to each other on paper. "Someday," he thought, "my people must learn to put our words on such talking leaves."

After the American Revolution, the Americans started fighting against England again. Sequoyah and some other Cherokee men joined the American army. Sequoyah noticed that the American soldiers could write letters to their loved ones and read letters sent from people back home. But the Cherokee soldiers had no way of writing their words to their families back home.

After the war, Sequoyah devoted himself to finding a way for the Cherokee people to be able to write down their words. At first, he tried to draw a picture to stand for every word. Imagine if you tried to draw a picture for every word you know! How long do you think it would take you? Well, Sequoyah drew hundreds and hundreds of pictures. Then he realized that the picture writing was too hard—no one would ever be able to learn to write this way.

Sequoyah kept trying. Day and night he scratched his ideas on paper. His friends and family members said, "What has gotten into you, Sequoyah? You're so caught up with your talking leaves that we never see you any more."

Finally, Sequoyah came up with an idea that worked. He invented a way to write the Cherokee language by using signs to stand for the different sounds in the language. He called his little daughter, Ayoka, to his side, and said, "Look, I will write my name. In my name, there are three sounds: Se-quoy-ah." Then he quickly made three little marks next to each other. "You see?" he said. "That says 'Sequoyah.' Now I'll write your name—Ayoka."

Sequoyah taught his daughter how to read and write the Cherokee language. Then he took Ayoka with him to see the leaders of the Cherokee Nation.

At first, the leaders did not believe his way of writing could work. They decided to give Sequoyah a test. They made Ayoka leave the room. Each leader told Sequoyah a story. Sequoyah wrote each story down on a piece of paper. Then Ayoka came back in. To the great surprise of the leaders, the little girl looked at the papers and read every word they had told Sequoyah!

Soon, many Cherokee people were learning to read and write their language. They wrote down their stories and their songs. They published newspapers, magazines, and books, all using the way of writing that Sequoyah worked so long and hard to invent.

AMERICAN LEGENDS: STORIES OF WASHINGTON IRVING

RIP VAN WINKLE
by Washington Irving

1

Whoever has made a voyage up the Hudson must remember the Catskill Mountains. Every change of season, every change of weather, indeed, every hour of the day produces some change in the magical hues and shapes of these mountains. When the sky is fair, the mountains are clothed in blue and purple. They print their bold outlines on the clear evening sky. But sometimes they will gather a hood of gray mist about their summits, which, in the last rays of the setting sun, will glow and light up like a crown of glory.

At the foot of these fairy mountains, a traveler may see wisps of smoke curling up from a village, founded by some of the first Dutch colonists. Some of the original settlers' houses still stand. They are built of small yellow bricks brought from Holland, with latticed windows and gable fronts, each topped with a weathercock.

In that same village, and in one of these very houses (which, to tell the truth, was sadly timeworn and weather-beaten), there once lived a simple good-natured fellow by the name of Rip Van Winkle.

Rip was a great favorite among the men and women. The children would shout with joy whenever he approached. Rip taught them to fly kites and shoot marbles. He told them long stories of strange adventures. Whenever he walked about the village, he was surrounded by a troop of them. They hung on his legs, clambered on his back, and played a thousand tricks on him. Not a dog would bark at him throughout the neighborhood.

The only trouble with Rip was that he did not like to work. Oh, he would sit on a wet rock and fish all day even if he didn't get a single nibble. He would carry a fowling piece on his shoulder for hours, trudging through woods and swamps, up hill and down dale, to shoot a few squirrels or wild pigeons. And he would never refuse to help a neighbor. But as to doing his family duty, and keeping his farm in order, he found it impossible. In short, Rip was ready to attend to everybody's business except his own.

Rip Van Winkle was one of those happy men who take the world easy. They eat white bread or brown, whichever can be got with least thought or trouble. They would rather starve on a penny than work for a pound.

If left to himself, he would have been perfectly content to whistle his life away. But his wife constantly shouted at him about his laziness, his carelessness, and the ruin he was bringing on his family. Morning, noon, and night, her tongue was busy scolding him, and a sharp tongue is the only edged tool that grows keener with constant use.

Rip had only one way of replying to her lectures. He shrugged his shoulders, shook his head, looked up to the sky, and said nothing. This made her even angrier, so he ended up taking to the outside of the house and the peace of the village streets.

Rip's walks usually ended at the village inn. On a bench before the inn, under a rubicund portrait of His Majesty

George the Third, some of the village men sat in the shade, talking over village gossip, or telling endless sleepy stories about nothing. The most respected of all these sages was Nicholas Vedder, the landlord of the inn. He sat at the door from morning till night, moving only enough to avoid the sun and keep in the shade of a large tree. The neighbors could tell the hour by his movements as accurately as by a sundial.

Vedder rarely spoke, and he smoked his pipe incessantly. Yet his friends understood him perfectly. When anything that was said displeased him, he smoked his pipe vehemently, sending forth short, angry puffs. When he was pleased, he would inhale the smoke slowly, and then blow out light, gentle clouds. Sometimes he would take the pipe from his mouth, let the fragrant smoke curl about his nose, and gravely nod his head.

But even from this friendly place, Rip was driven by his termagant wife. Nearly every afternoon, Dame Van Winkle would break in upon the group and shatter the peace of the day. She would shout at all the men, accusing them of encouraging Rip's laziness.

Poor Rip was at last reduced almost to despair. To escape from the labor of the farm and clamor of his wife, his only choice was to take gun in hand and stroll away into the woods with his dog, Wolf.

"Poor Wolf," Rip would say, "your Dame makes it a dog's life. But never mind, my boy. While I live, you will always have a friend to stand by you!" Wolf would wag his tail and look lovingly into his master's face. If dogs can feel pity, I believe Wolf returned the feeling with all his heart.

2

One fine autumn afternoon, Rip wandered up one of the highest peaks of the Catskill Mountains. He was after his favorite sport of squirrel shooting, and the still solitudes echoed with the reports of his gun. Late in the afternoon, panting and exhausted, he threw himself on a small green hill, near the edge of a cliff. On one side, he could see all the lower country for many miles around. He saw the lordly Hudson far, far below him, moving on its silent but majestic course until it disappeared into the blue mountains.

On the other side, he looked down into a wild mountain glen. He gazed deep into the glen, until the mountains began to throw their long blue shadows over the valleys. Rip saw that it would be dark long before he would reach the village, and he sighed when he thought of encountering the terrors of Dame Van Winkle.

As he was about to start down the mountain, he heard a voice hallooing, "Rip Van Winkle! Rip Van Winkle!" Rip turned, and saw nothing but a crow flying overhead.

He took another step, and heard, "Rip Van Winkle! Rip Van Winkle!"

Wolf bristled up his back, gave a low growl, and crept to his master's side. Rip felt a terrible fear stealing over him. Both Rip and Wolf looked nervously into the glen.

A strange figure appeared, slowly climbing the rocks. He was bent under the weight of something he carried on his back. Rip was surprised to see another human being in this lonely place. He thought it must be one of the villagers in need of his help, so he hurried down to offer a hand.

   As he got closer, he was still more surprised. The stranger
was a short, square-built old fellow, with thick bushy hair and
a grizzled beard. His clothes were of the old Dutch fashion,
like those worn by the settlers hundreds of years before. He
wore a cloth jerkin strapped round the waist, and a pair of
wide breeches decorated with rows of buttons down the sides.

   The stranger made signs for Rip to help him with the barrel
he carried. Though suspicious of the fellow, Rip moved

quickly to help him. Together they climbed higher into the Catskills. As they made their way up, every now and then Rip heard long rolling peals, like thunder, that seemed to come out of a deep ravine between the highest rocks.

During the whole time, Rip and his companion walked in silence. Though Rip greatly wondered what could be the reason for carrying a barrel up this wild mountain, there was something strange and mysterious that filled him with awe and made him reluctant to speak.

They passed through the ravine, which opened into a hollow. In the center was a group of the oddest-looking men, playing at ninepins. Some wore short doublets, while others wore jerkins with long knives in their belts. Most of them wore enormous breeches, like the man Rip had followed.

Their faces, too, were peculiar. One had a large beard, broad face, and small, piggish eyes. The face of another seemed to consist entirely of nose, and was topped by a white sugar-loaf hat with a little red cock's tail. They all had beards of various shapes and colors.

There was one who seemed to be the commander. He was a stout old gentleman with a weather-beaten face. He wore a laced doublet, broad belt, high crowned hat and feather, red stockings, and high-heeled shoes with roses in them. The whole group reminded Rip of something out of an old painting that he had seen in the village.

What seemed particularly odd to Rip was that though these folks seemed to be amusing themselves, their faces were grave, and they kept a mysterious silence. Nothing interrupted the stillness but the noise of the balls, which, whenever they were rolled, echoed along the mountains like rumbling peals of thunder.

As Rip and the man approached them, they suddenly stopped their play. They turned and stared at Rip. Rip's heart turned within him, and his knees knocked together.

The man filled large flagons with liquid from the barrel. Then he made signs for Rip to serve the company. He obeyed with fear and trembling. The strange men quaffed their drinks in terrible silence, then returned to their game.

Slowly, Rip's fear relaxed its hold on him. When no one was looking, he even dared to taste the liquid in one of the flagons. One taste led to another, and another, and another. Before he knew it, his eyes swam in his head, and he fell into a deep sleep.

When Rip awoke, he found himself near the glen where he had first seen the strange man. He rubbed his eyes. It was a bright sunny morning. The birds were hopping and twittering among the bushes.

"Surely, I have not slept here all night," thought Rip.

He tried to remember what happened before he fell asleep. The strange man with the barrel—the mountain hollow—the strange, sad men playing at ninepins—the flagon. "Oh, that flagon! That wicked flagon!" thought Rip. "What excuse shall I make to Dame Van Winkle?"

He looked round for his gun, but in place of the clean, well-oiled fowling piece, he found only an old firelock lying by him. The barrel was encrusted with rust, the lock was falling off, and the stock was worm-eaten. He now suspected that the grave men of the mountain had played a trick on him. Perhaps they had waited till he fell asleep, then robbed him of his gun.

Wolf, too, had disappeared, but he might have strayed away after a squirrel or partridge. Rip whistled after him and shouted his name, but all in vain. The echoes repeated his whistle and shout, but no dog was to be seen.

He decided to go back to the hollow. If he met any of the strange men, he would demand his dog and gun. As he rose to walk, he felt stiff and sore. "These mountain beds do not agree with me," thought Rip.

With some difficulty he got down into the glen and found the path he and the man had followed. But to his surprise, a mountain stream was now foaming down it, leaping from rock to rock.

Rip scrambled up the sides of the stream to where the ravine had opened into the hollow. But the hollow was filled with rocks. And over the rocks, a waterfall tumbled in a sheet of feathery foam.

Here, then, poor Rip was brought to a standstill. Again he called and whistled after his dog. He was only answered by the cawing of a flock of crows.

What was to be done? The morning was passing away, and Rip was hungry. He was sad to give up his dog and gun, he was terrified of meeting his wife, but it would not do to starve in the mountains. Rip shook his head, shouldered the rusty firelock, and with a heart full of worry, turned his steps homeward.

3

As he approached the village he met a number of people, but none whom he knew. This surprised him. He thought he knew everyone in the country round. Their dress, too, was strange.

They all stared at him with equal surprise. And whenever they looked, they stroked their chins. At last, Rip did the same, and, to his astonishment, found that his beard had grown a foot long!

He had now entered the village. A troop of strange children ran at his heels. They hooted at him and pointed at his gray beard. He did not recognize even one of the dogs. They all barked at him as he passed.

Even the village was changed. It was larger and full of people. There were rows of houses he had never seen before. Strange names were over the doors, strange faces were at the windows. Everything was strange.

But surely this was his village he had left but the day before! There stood the Catskill Mountains; there ran the silver Hudson; there was every hill and dale just as it had always been.

Rip was very confused. "That flagon last night," thought he, "has addled my poor head!"

It took Rip some time to find his own house. He tiptoed near, expecting every moment that Dame Van Winkle would fly out of the house and scold him.

But he found the house ruined. The roof had fallen in. The windows were shattered. The doors were off the hinges. A half-starved dog that looked like Wolf crept out of the shadows. Rip called him by name, but the cur snarled, showed his teeth, and passed on. This was unkind indeed. "My very dog," sighed poor Rip, "has forgotten me!"

He entered the house, which Dame Van Winkle had always kept in neat order. Now dusty cobwebs stretched in every corner. Rip called loudly for his wife and children. The lonely house rang for a moment with his voice. Then all again was silence.

He hurried to the village inn, but it, too, was gone. A large, rickety wooden building stood in its place, and over the door was painted, "The Union Hotel." Instead of the great tree that used to shade the quiet little Dutch inn, there now stood a tall pole, with something on the top that looked like a red nightcap. From it was fluttering a flag, covered with stars and stripes. Still, Rip recognized on the sign the ruby face of King George under which he had smoked so many a peaceful pipe. But even this was transformed. The red coat was changed for one of blue, a sword was held in the hand instead of a scepter, and underneath was painted in large letters, *GENERAL Washington.*

There was, as usual, a crowd of folk about the door. But Rip did not recognize any of them. He looked for Nicholas Vedder, with his broad face, double chin, and long pipe. But instead he saw a skinny young fellow. He was making an angry speech about the rights of citizens, members of Congress, liberty, Bunker Hill, the heroes of seventy-six, and other words that were nothing but a puzzle to poor, bewildered Rip Van Winkle.

A self-important old gentleman in a cocked hat made his way through the crowd. Planting himself before Rip Van Winkle, he asked in a sharp tone, "What brings you to the election with a gun on your shoulder and a mob at your heels? Do you mean to breed a riot in the village?"

"Alas, gentlemen!" cried Rip, "I am a poor quiet man, a native of the place, and a loyal subject of King George, God bless him!"

Here a general shout burst from the bystanders. "A Tory! A Tory! A spy! Away with him!" It was with great difficulty that the self-important man in the cocked hat restored order. Again he demanded that Rip explain what he came there for, and whom he was seeking.

"Please," said Rip, "I am looking for some of my neighbors who used to gather about this tavern."

"Well, who are they? What are their names?"

Rip asked, "Where's Nicholas Vedder?"

There was a silence for a little while, when an old man replied, in a thin piping voice, "Nicholas Vedder! Why, he is dead and gone these eighteen years! There was a wooden tombstone in the churchyard that used to tell all about him, but that's rotten and gone too."

"Where's Brom Dutcher?"

"Oh, he went off to the army in the beginning of the war, and never came back again."

"Where's Van Bummel, the schoolmaster?"

"He went off to the war too, was a great general, and is now in Congress."

Rip's heart died away at hearing of these sad changes in his home and friends, and finding himself alone in the world. But the answers puzzled him, too. Where had the time gone? What was this news of war, armies, and Congress?

He had no courage to ask after any more friends. But he cried out in despair, "Does nobody here know Rip Van Winkle?"

"Oh, Rip Van Winkle!" exclaimed two or three, "Oh, to be sure! That's Rip Van Winkle there, leaning against the tree."

Rip looked, and saw an exact copy of himself from the day he went up to the mountain. The poor fellow was now completely confused. He did not know who he was, and whether he was himself or another man.

In the midst of his bewilderment, the man in the cocked hat demanded, "Who are you? Tell us, now, what is your name?"

"God knows," exclaimed poor Rip, at his wit's end, "I'm not myself—I'm somebody else—that's me yonder—no—

that's somebody else got into my shoes—I was myself last night, but I fell asleep on the mountain, and they've changed my gun, and everything's changed, and I'm changed, and I can't tell what's my name, or who I am!"

4

At this moment, a pretty woman pressed through the crowd to have a look at the gray-bearded stranger. She had a chubby child in her arms, which, frightened at his looks, began to cry. "Hush, Rip," said she, "hush, child, the old man won't hurt you."

The name of the child, the face of the mother, the tone of her voice, all awakened a train of memories. "What is your name, my good woman?" asked Rip.

"Judith Gardener."

"And your father's name?"

"Ah, poor man, Rip Van Winkle was his name. But it's twenty years since he went away from home with his gun, and has never been heard of since. I was then but a little girl. His dog came home without him, but no one knows what happened to him. There stands his son, also called Rip Van Winkle, by the tree. A perfect copy of his father, he is."

Rip had one question more to ask. "Where's your mother?"

"Oh, she died a short time ago. She broke a blood vessel in a fit of anger at a New England peddler."

The honest man could contain himself no longer. He caught his daughter and her child in his arms. "I'm your father!" he cried. "Young Rip Van Winkle once—old Rip Van Winkle now! Does nobody know Rip Van Winkle?"

All stood amazed. An old woman, tottering out from among the crowd, put her hand to her brow and peered at his face for a moment. Then she exclaimed, "Sure enough! It

is Rip Van Winkle—it is himself! Welcome home again, old neighbor. Why, where have you been these twenty long years?"

Rip's story was soon told, for the whole twenty years had been to him but as one night. The neighbors stared when they heard it. Some winked at each other, and put their tongues in their cheeks. The old gentleman shook his head, which then caused a chain of head shaking in the crowd.

At that moment, up the road came old Peter Vanderdonk. He was the oldest person in the village, and he knew all the wonderful events and traditions of the neighborhood.

Old Peter recognized Rip at once. Not only did he confirm Rip's story, he also told the crowd that the Catskill Mountains had always been the home of strange beings. Rip, said Peter, had seen the great Hendrick Hudson himself, the first European discoverer of the river and surrounding countryside. Old Peter said that Hudson came back every twenty years with his ghostly crew to play at ninepins and watch over the river and the great city called by his name. Peter's father had once seen them in their old Dutch dresses playing at ninepins in a hollow of the mountain. Peter himself had heard, one summer afternoon, the sound of their balls, like distant peals of thunder.

With that, the crowd broke up and returned to the more important concerns of the election. Rip's daughter took him home to live with her. She had a snug, well-furnished house, and a stout cheery farmer for a husband, whom Rip recalled as one of the children who used to climb upon his back.

Rip now took up his old walks and habits. He soon found many of his old friends, but they were all rather the worse for the wear and tear of time. He preferred making friends among the younger folk, with whom he soon grew into great favor.

Having nothing to do at home, he took his place once more on the bench at the inn door. The villagers treated him with special respect, because he remembered the old times "before the war." It was some time before he came to understand the strange events that had taken place during his absence. There had been a revolutionary war. The country had thrown off the yoke of old England, and now, instead of being a subject of His Majesty George the Third, Rip was a free citizen of the United States.

Rip told his story to every stranger who arrived at the hotel. He was observed at first to vary on some points every time he told it, no doubt because he had so recently awaked. At last, every man, woman, and child in the neighborhood

knew it by heart. Some always pretended to doubt the truth of it. They insisted that Rip had been out of his head. But the old Dutch inhabitants believed Rip was telling the truth.

Even to this day, when they hear a thunderstorm on a summer afternoon in the mountains, they say that Hendrick Hudson and his crew are playing their game of ninepins. And it is a common wish of all henpecked husbands in the neighborhood, when life hangs heavy on their hands, that they might have a quieting drink from Rip Van Winkle's flagon.

THE LEGEND OF SLEEPY HOLLOW
by Washington Irving

1

On the eastern shore of the Hudson, by the wide Tappan Zee, there is a little valley among high hills. It is one of the quietest places in the whole world. A small brook glides through it, murmuring to lull one to sleep. The whistle of a quail or tapping of a woodpecker is almost the only sound that ever breaks the unchanging silence. This quiet glen has long been known by the name of Sleepy Hollow. A drowsy, dreamy feeling seems to hang over the land. One can almost feel it in the air. If ever I should wish to get away from world and its troubles, I know no place better than this little valley.

There is, however, something strange about this place. Stars shoot and meteors glare more across this valley than in any other part of the country. The people walk around as though they are in a dream. They are given to all kinds of marvelous beliefs. The whole neighborhood abounds with tales and superstitions.

But the most famous figure in Sleepy Hollow is the apparition of a man on horseback. Some say it is the ghost of a Hessian soldier, whose head was carried away by a cannonball in a battle during the Revolutionary War.

The folk of this enchanted region believe that the soldier's body was buried in their churchyard. Every night, they say, his ghost rides forth to the scene of battle in search of his head.

Sometimes the wind rushes through the Hollow like a midnight blast. They say it is because the soldier is late, and in a hurry to get back to the churchyard before daybreak.

That is what the Hollow folk tell of the strange and shadowy legend of the Headless Horseman of Sleepy Hollow.

2

The Hollow has a strange, dreamy effect on both its residents and the visitors to its valley. One such visitor was a schoolteacher named Ichabod Crane.

The name Crane suited Ichabod well. He was tall, but very thin. He had narrow shoulders and long arms and legs. His hands dangled a mile out of his sleeves. His feet might have served for shovels. His whole frame was most loosely hung together.

His head was small, and flat at top, with huge ears, a long snipe nose, and large green glassy eyes. It looked like a weathercock perched upon his skinny neck to tell which way the wind blew. To see him striding over a hill on a windy day, with his clothes fluttering about him, one might have mistaken him for a scarecrow escaping from a cornfield.

Ichabod Crane's schoolhouse was one large room, rudely made of logs. The windows were partly glazed, and partly patched with pages from old copybooks. On a drowsy summer's day, one could hear the pupils' voices practicing their lessons, murmuring like the hum of a beehive.

When school hours were over, Ichabod played with the boys, especially if they had pretty sisters, or mothers who were excellent cooks. Indeed, he had to keep on good terms with his pupils. He made little money teaching. It would have hardly been enough to feed him.

Ichabod had a tremendous appetite. He could stuff himself like an anaconda. But it was the custom of the Hollow folk to give a room and meals to their children's schoolmaster. So he lived with each family a week at a time, going round the neighborhood, with all his belongings tied up in a cotton handkerchief.

Ichabod was also the singing-master of the neighborhood. He earned many bright shillings giving the young folks lessons. His greatest joy was to take his band of chosen singers to the front of the church on Sunday.

Certain it is, his voice was heard far above all the rest. Even now, there are peculiar quavers still to be heard in that church. On a quiet Sunday morning, one can hear them half a mile away. They are said to be echoes from the nose of Ichabod Crane.

Ichabod was also a kind of traveling gazette. He carried all the local gossip from house to house. He had read several books quite through. And he was also a perfect master of all the strange, dark stories of the country round.

It was often his delight, after his school was dismissed in the afternoon, to stretch himself out by the little brook beside his schoolhouse. There he read books of frightening tales until evening. Then he made his way through the dark hills to the farmhouse where he was staying.

As he walked, every sound of nature fluttered his excited imagination. The moan of the whippoorwill from the hillside, the hooting of the screech owl, and the sudden rustling of birds in the thicket filled him with terror. Fireflies startled him. If a foolish beetle flew into him, poor Ichabod practically died of fright.

To drive away his fears, he sang psalm tunes. And the Hollow folk often heard his melodies floating up from the road as they sat by their doors in the evening.

Ichabod also enjoyed talking with the old Dutch wives as they sat spinning by their fires. He listened to their tales of ghosts and goblins, haunted fields, haunted brooks, haunted bridges, and haunted houses. He particularly enjoyed tales of the Headless Horseman.

But for the pleasure of hearing these tales, he paid the price of the terrors of his walk home. What fearful shapes and shadows crossed his path in the dimness of a snowy night! How terrified he was that some rushing blast, howling among the trees, might be the Headless Horseman on one of his nightly rides!

3

Ichabod's fears were only terrors of the night. Daylight put an end to all his imaginings. He would have passed a pleasant life of it, too, if Katrina Van Tassel had not crossed his path.

Katrina Van Tassel was a blooming lass of fresh eighteen. She was rosy-cheeked as one of her father's peaches, and known for her beauty as well as her father's wealth. Ichabod Crane yearned after the girl and her father's fat meadowlands. He dreamed of selling the rich fields and the orchards heavy with ruddy fruit. He would use the money to buy wild land to the west. He imagined Katrina and a whole family of children sitting on the top of a wagon loaded with furniture. He saw himself riding a beautiful horse, with a colt at its heels, setting out for Kentucky, Tennessee, or who knows where!

Ichabod longed to win the heart of old Van Tassel's daughter. But Katrina had a number of admirers already. They kept a watchful and angry eye upon each other. They were always ready to fly out against any new suitor.

Among these, the most formidable was a burly, roaring man named Abraham Van Brunt, or, as the Dutch called him, Brom. He was the hero of the country round. And for his Herculean strength, he had been nicknamed Brom Bones.

Brom was famed for his great skill on horseback. He was first at all the races, and always ready for either a fight or fun. He had more mischief than ill will in his character. With all his roughness, there was a strong dash of good humor at bottom.

The neighbors looked upon him with a mixture of awe, admiration, and good will. When any madcap prank occurred, they shook their heads, and thought that Brom Bones must be at the bottom of it.

Sometimes Brom and his crew dashed past the farmhouses at midnight, whooping and hallooing. When the hurry-scurry had clattered by, the Hollow folk exclaimed, "Ay, there goes Brom Bones and his gang!"

Brom had for some time courted the blooming Katrina. He was Ichabod's chief rival. A braver man than Ichabod would have shrunk from the competition. A wiser man would have given up entirely. But Ichabod was both flexible and determined. He bent but never broke. Though he bowed beneath the slightest pressure, the moment it was away, he carried his head as high as ever.

Certain it is, when Ichabod Crane began courting Katrina, Brom's horse was no longer seen at the farmhouse in the evenings. And a deadly feud gradually arose between Brom Bones and the schoolmaster of Sleepy Hollow.

Brom would have fought Ichabod for Katrina, like the knights of long ago. But Ichabod would not fight.

So Brom Bones and his gang of rough riders played pranks on Ichabod. They broke into the schoolhouse at night. They stopped up the chimney and turned everything topsy-turvy. Brom even had a dog that he taught to whine in the most ridiculous manner. Then he introduced it to Katrina as a rival of Ichabod's, to give her singing lessons.

Matters went on this way for some time. Then, one fine autumn afternoon, while Ichabod sat enthroned on a lofty stool at the head of his students, a servant of the Van Tassels appeared at the door. He invited Ichabod to attend a merry-making or "quilting-frolic" at their farmhouse that evening.

Ichabod sent his students home early and closed up the schoolhouse. He spent at least an extra half hour making himself look his best. Since he wanted to look like a knight to Katrina, he also borrowed a horse from the farmer with whom he was staying.

I must give some account of the looks of our hero and his steed. The animal he rode was an old, broken-down plow-horse. He was gaunt and shaggy, with a thin neck and a head like a hammer. His rusty mane and tail were tangled and knotted with burs. His one good eye had the gleam of a genuine devil in it. Still he must have had fire and mettle in his day, if we may judge by his name, Gunpowder.

Ichabod was a suitable figure for such a steed. He rode with short stirrups, which brought his knees nearly up to the top of the saddle. His sharp elbows stuck out like grasshoppers' legs. He carried his whip in his hand like a scepter. As his horse jogged on, the motion of his arms was like the flapping of a pair of wings.

It was toward evening that Ichabod arrived at the home of Heer Van Tassel. There were old farmers in homespun coats and breeches, blue stockings, huge shoes, and magnificent pewter buckles. There were their brisk little dames, in close-crimped caps and short gowns with calico pockets on the outside. Their beautiful daughters dressed the same, except where a straw hat or a fine ribbon dared the local fashion.

Brom Bones, however, was the hero of the scene. He had come to the gathering on his favorite steed, Daredevil. Daredevil was a creature like himself, full of mettle and mischief. No one but Brom could manage him.

But Ichabod only had eyes for the supper table. There was the doughty doughnut, and the crisp and crumbling cruller. There were the sweet cakes and short cakes, ginger cakes and honey cakes. There were the apple pies, and peach pies, and pumpkin pies, slices of ham and smoked beef, and dishes of preserved plums, peaches, pears, and quinces. Not to mention the broiled fish and roasted chickens, bowls of milk and cream, all mingled higgledy-piggledy, with the motherly teapot sending up clouds of vapor from the midst!

Happily, Ichabod Crane was not in so great a hurry as I am. He lingered over every tasty dish.

Then the fiddler began to play and stamp his foot. Couples whirled into the dance. Ichabod prided himself on his dancing as much as upon his singing. Not a limb, not a fiber on him was idle. To have seen his loosely hung frame in full motion, clattering about the room, you would have thought St. Vitus himself was dancing before you in person.

Katrina, the lady of his heart, was his partner. She smiled at him graciously. But Brom Bones, sorely smitten with love and jealousy, sat brooding by himself in a corner.

4

When the dance was at an end, Ichabod joined a group of folks who were gossiping over old times and telling long stories about the Revolutionary War. Sleepy Hollow was a place around which great men had done great deeds. The British and Americans had run near it during the war. And just enough time had passed for each storyteller to dress up his tale and make himself the hero of every adventure.

But all these stories paled in comparison to the dark tales of the favorite specter of Sleepy Hollow, the Headless Horseman. Some said that lately he had been heard several times galloping round the country.

Brom Bones himself said that one night he had seen the Headless Horseman, and dared him to race. He said he should have won, too, for Daredevil had beaten the goblin horse. But just as they came to the church bridge, the Hessian bolted, and vanished in a flash of fire.

Ichabod added a great many tales of his own to these. But the men's words sank deep into his mind.

The party slowly broke up. Each headed his way in a wagon or on foot, rattling along the roads and over the distant hills. Ichabod stayed behind to talk with Katrina. What they said I do not know, but something must have gone wrong, because he left, crestfallen, shortly after. He roused his steed from the stable and began his ride home.

Under the darkening skies, all the terrifying stories he had heard in the afternoon now came crowding into his mind. He had never felt so lonely and dismal. Suddenly he heard a groan. Ichabod's teeth chattered. His knees knocked against the saddle. But the noise was only the rubbing of one tree branch against another, as they were swayed about by the breeze.

Then, as he approached the bridge, he saw something huge and towering in the shadows. It did not stir, but it seemed to gather up in the gloom, like some gigantic monster ready to spring upon him.

Ichabod's hair rose with terror. What was to be done? It was too late to turn and flee. Besides, what chance was there of escaping a ghost or goblin, if such it was, that could ride upon the wings of the wind?

Making a show of courage, Ichabod demanded, "Who are you?" He received no reply.

Ichabod shut his eyes and began singing a psalm tune. Just then the shadowy thing put itself in motion. With a scramble

and a bound, it stood at once in the middle of the road.
It appeared to be a huge horseman, mounted on a powerful
black horse. He said no word, but jogged along beside
old Gunpowder.

Ichabod remembered the adventure of Brom Bones with
the Headless Horseman. He spurred his own horse, hoping
to leave his strange midnight companion behind. But the
stranger quickened his horse to an equal pace.

Ichabod pulled up, and fell into a walk, thinking to lag
behind. The horseman did the same. Ichabod's heart began to
sink within him. He tried to sing, but his parched tongue
stuck to the roof of his mouth. He could not utter a note.

As they broke through the trees, Ichabod saw his fellow
traveler in relief against the sky. He was gigantic in height,
and muffled in a cloak. But Ichabod was horror-struck when
he saw that the horseman was headless! His horror grew when
he saw that the head, which should have rested on his
shoulders, was carried before him on the pommel of his saddle!

Ichabod's terror rose to desperation. He rained a shower of
kicks and blows upon Gunpowder. He hoped to give the
horseman the slip. But the specter kept pace with him.

Away they dashed through thick and thin. Stones flew and
sparks flashed at every bound.

So far, Gunpowder's panic had given Ichabod a few
steps ahead in the chase. But just as he got halfway through
the hollow, the girth of the saddle broke. The saddle fell to
the ground. He heard it trampled underfoot by the
monstrous horseman.

Ichabod had much ado to stay on the horse's back.
Sometimes he slipped to one side, sometimes to another. And
sometimes he was jolted on the high ridge of his horse's
backbone with a violence that he feared would split him in two.

An opening in the trees now cheered him with the hopes that the church bridge was near. He saw the walls of the church dimly glaring under the trees beyond. He remembered the place where Brom Bones's ghostly competitor had disappeared. "If I can only reach that bridge," thought Ichabod, " I am safe."

Just then he heard the black steed panting and blowing close behind him. He fancied that he felt the horse's hot breath.

Another kick in the ribs, and old Gunpowder sprang upon the bridge. He thundered over the planks and reached the opposite side.

Ichabod looked behind him to see if his pursuer would vanish, as the stories told, in a flash of fire. But just then he saw the thing rising in its stirrups. It drew back its hand to hurl its head at Ichabod.

Ichabod tried to dodge the horrible missile, but too late. It hit the terrified schoolteacher's head with a tremendous crash. He tumbled into the dust. Gunpowder, the black steed, and the horseman passed by like a whirlwind.

5

The next morning the old horse was found without his saddle, nibbling the grass at his master's gate. Ichabod did not appear at breakfast or at the schoolhouse. The Hollow folk searched for him. But they found only the saddle trampled in the dirt, the tracks of horses' hoofs deeply dented in the road, the hat of the unfortunate Ichabod, and close beside it, a shattered pumpkin.

The mysterious event caused much talk at the church the following Sunday. Knots of gazers and gossips were collected in the churchyard, at the bridge, and at the spot where the hat and pumpkin had been found. They shook their heads and came to the conclusion that Ichabod had been carried off by the Headless Horseman.

Some years later, an old farmer said that Ichabod Crane was still alive. He said that the schoolmaster had left the Hollow partly through fear of the horseman, and partly in embarrassment at being jilted by Katrina. The farmer said Ichabod had moved far away and became a judge in a court.

Shortly after Ichabod disappeared, Brom Bones married Katrina. And, whenever the story of Ichabod was related, he always got a very knowing look and burst into a hearty laugh at the mention of the pumpkin. It led some to suspect that he knew more about the matter than he chose to tell.

The old country wives, however, who are the best judges of these matters, maintain to this day that Ichabod was spirited away by supernatural means. It is a favorite story often told about the neighborhood round the winter evening fire. The schoolhouse has since fallen into decay, and has been reported to be haunted by Ichabod's ghost. And on a still summer evening, some say they hear Ichabod's voice at a distance, chanting a melancholy psalm tune among the tranquil solitudes of Sleepy Hollow.

TEXT CREDITS AND SOURCES

"Young Benjamin Franklin" adapted from *Barnes's Elementary History of the United States Told in Biographies* by James Baldwin (New York: American Book Company, 1908); and, *Expressive Readers—Fifth Reader* by James Baldwin and Ida C. Bender (New York: American Book Company, 1911).

"A Poem to King George" reprinted with the permission of Aladdin Paperbacks, an imprint of Simon & Schuster Children's Publishing Division from *Phyllis Wheatley: Young Colonial Poet* by Kathryn Kilby Borland and Helen Ross Speicher, copyright © 1968 Bobbs-Merrill Company.

"Sybil Ludington: The Female Paul Revere" by Patricia Edwards Clyne from *Patriots in Petticoats* by Patricia Edwards Clyne, copyright © 1976. Reprinted by permission of Patricia Edwards Clyne.

"Sequoyah's Great Invention" by Vanessa Wright for K12.

While every care has been taken to trace and acknowledge copyright, the editors tender their apologies for any accidental infringement when copyright has proven untraceable. They would be pleased to include the appropriate acknowledgement in any subsequent edition of this publication.

Editor: John Holdren

Art Director: Steve Godwin

Designer: Jayoung Cho

Illustrators:
Jayoung Cho
Deborah Wolfe Ltd: (Jerry Dadds, Nancy Harrison, Jim Hays, Phillip Small)

ISBN: 1-931728-40-2